Comprehen

Ages 5–6

Irene Yates

HOPSCOTCH
EDUCATIONAL PUBLISHING

Published by Hopscotch
A division of MA Education Ltd
St Jude's Church
Dulwich Road
Herne Hill
London SE24 0PB

Tel: 020 7738 5454

© 2007 MA Education Ltd

Written by Irene Yates
Series design by Blade Communications
Illustrated by Catherine Ward
Printed by Cle-print, Huntingdon

ISBN 1-905390-00-9
ISBN13 978-1-905390-00-7

Irene Yates hereby asserts her moral right to be identified as the
author of this work in accordance with the Copyright, Designs
and Patents Act, 1988.

The National Literacy Strategy Framework – Text level links for Year 1

	T1	T2	T3	T4	T5	T6	T7	T8	T9	T10	T11	T12	T13	T14	T15	T16	T17	T18	T19	T20	T21	T22	T23	T24	T25	T26	T27
Term 1 Activity 1a		•																									
Activity 1b		•																									
Activity 1c		•																									
Activity 2a						•																					
Activity 2b						•																					
Activity 2c						•																					
Activity 3a												•															
Activity 3b												•															
Activity 3c												•															
Activity 4a					•																						
Activity 4b					•																						
Activity 4c					•																						
Activity 5a													•														
Activity 5b													•														
Activity 5c													•														
Activity 6a							•																				
Activity 6b							•																				
Activity 6c							•																				
Activity 7a	•																										
Activity 7b	•																										
Activity 7c	•																										
Term 2 Activity 8a								•																			
Activity 8b								•																			
Activity 8c								•																			
Activity 9a																			•								
Activity 9b																			•								
Activity 9c																			•								
Activity 10a											•																
Activity 10b											•																
Activity 10c											•																
Activity 11a									•																		
Activity 11b									•																		
Activity 11c									•																		
Activity 12a							•																				
Activity 12b							•																				
Activity 12c							•																				
Activity 13a																	•										
Activity 13b																	•										
Activity 13c																	•										
Activity 14a																				•							
Activity 14b																				•							
Activity 14c																				•							
Term 3 Activity 15a	•																										
Activity 15b	•																										
Activity 15c	•																										
Activity 16a							•																				
Activity 16b							•																				
Activity 16c							•																				
Activity 17a																	•										
Activity 17b																	•										
Activity 17c																	•										
Activity 18a																					•						
Activity 18b																					•						
Activity 18c																					•						
Activity 19a					•																						
Activity 19b					•																						
Activity 19c					•																						
Activity 20a								•																			
Activity 20b								•																			
Activity 20c								•																			
Activity 21a																		•									
Activity 21b																		•									
Activity 21c																		•									
Activity 22a									•																		
Activity 22b									•																		
Activity 22c									•																		

INTRODUCTION

'Comprehension is the ultimate goal of reading'
Primary Framework for Literacy – September 2006

This book explores the 'Understanding and Interpreting Texts' and the 'Engaging with and Responding to Texts' strands of the nenewed *Primary Literacy Framework*. It is also cross-referenced to the Literacy Strategy's text level objectives. These text level objectives are the basis for the activities in this book. The book is not intended as an individual work book. Its concept is that an adult will be working with the child, at whichever stage, in order to facilitate their understanding and their ability to process and answer the questions, simultaneously developing their reading and writing skills as they work through the pages.

Each activity should be discussed, with the child verbalising what they understand from the pictures or the texts, the adult pointing out what they miss and encouraging them to verbalise answers to the questions before attempting to write or having the adult scribe for them.

As the adult goes through the text with the child, she should encourage the child to become familiar with and recognise the various features of words: initial sounds, digraphs, double and triple consonants, vowels, final sounds and so on, and help the child to a) build up words and b) predict words from knowledge of some of the graphic details and from the context. In this way the activities become much more than just a comprehension task and help the child to absorb the many strategies that they may use in learning to read.

It is important for the children to learn to form their answers in simple but full sentences – ie those with at least a subject and a verb. They will then assimilate from this early stage that this is the way to answer comprehension questions.

The following notes give guidance for each activity.

Activity 1 – Y1, Term 1, T2

1a – Make sure the children know the story. Give them plenty of time to look at the picture. Ask them to point out all the things they can see. Explain that they are going to put a cross or a tick in the correct boxes when you read the questions to them. Ask them to identify the words 'Yes' and 'No' for themselves. Give clear instructions for the rest of the tasks.
1b – Read the tasks but help the children to identify as many words as they can by just cueing in the sounds. Encourage them to locate the appropriate words and copy them into the spaces. Encourage lateral thinking skills for the last question.
1c – Make sure the children can read the text, helping where necessary. Go over words that are unfamiliar. Read the questions together before working on the answers. Help the children to verbalise the answers then write them. Scribe for the child when appropriate.

Activity 2 – Y1, Term 1, T6

2a – Give lots of time to 'read' the picture with children verbalising what they can see. Say the rhyme together, paying attention to the pattern and metre. Give clear instructions for the tasks.
2b – Give time for the children to verbalise the picture. Encourage suggestions about which rhyme it might be about. Encourage them to read by predicting the words from the initial sounds. Tap the rhythm of the rhyme out together.
2c – Read the words of the rhyme together, paying attention to the rhythm and the second verse, which the children may not know. Discuss the tasks and help the children to verbalise before writing the answers.

Activity 3 – Y1, Term 1, T12

3a – Talk about what the teacher is doing in the picture. Discuss 'labels' and 'captions' to make sure the children know what they are. Make sure the children understand that the words under their pictures at the bottom of the sheet are captions.
3b – Discuss the idea of labels, captions and notices. Help the children to locate those words in the questions. Get them to verbalise before writing or scribing.
3c – Read the notice and the text together. Discuss the questions before deciding on answers. Help children to verbalise in proper sentences.

Activity 4 – Y1, Term 1, T5

4a – Discuss the picture, emphasising the 'where' and the 'when'. Read the questions through with the children and help them to verbalise before writing or scribing.
4b – Discuss the picture, asking the children 'where' and 'when' questions. If they were in the picture, which sounds would they hear? Read the questions through with them before they try to answer them.
4c – Read the story together. Ask the children, 'Where is it happening? When is it happening?' Read through the questions with them. Use the word 'setting' when appropriate.

Activity 5 – Y1, Term 1, T13

5a – Carefully go through the pictures with the children. What do they think the pictures are telling them? Use the word 'instructions' and make sure they understand it. Help them to complete the tasks.
5b – Ask the children what the pictures are telling them. Encourage use of the word 'instructions'. Help them to read and answer the tasks, then follow the instructions.
5c – Ask the children what kind of text this is. Make sure they can read all of it, including the questions. Help them to verbalise before writing. Encourage them to follow the instructions to make a mask.

Activity 6 – Y1, Term 1, T7

6a – Make sure that the children understand that Jake's class are making up a play for the mums and dads.

When they have answered all the questions and know the story within the story, encourage them to improvise the play.

6b – Ask the children to verbalise what is happening in the picture before attempting the tasks. Encourage them to re-enact the story.

6c – Encourage the children to read all the text and all the tasks before working on them. Try to find out whether they understand that this is a story about pirates within a story about children. When they re-enact the story, which will they do?

Activity 7 – Y1, Term 1, T1

7a – Share the story with a small group by discussing what is happening in the pictures. Help the children to reach consensus on the tasks.

7b – Help the children to work together to read the pictures and to decide on how to complete the tasks. Give them each a chance to verbalise before writing or you scribing for them.

7c – Get the children to work in pairs to read the text together, discuss the tasks and formulate their answers before writing.

Activity 8 – Y1, Term 2, T8

8a – Help the children to verbalise what is happening in the picture. Familiarise them with the words 'Yes' and 'No'. Read the questions clearly. Encourage them to verbalise the answers before writing.

8b – Ask the children to tell you what they can see and read the speech bubbles together. Who is the story about? Assist the children in matching the words in order to fill in the spaces. Help them to complete the other tasks on the sheet.

8c – Make sure the children can read the text and the questions. Reinforce any difficult words. Help them to look for the answers within the text.

Activity 9 – Y1, Term 2, T19

9a – Help the children to read the picture and predict what might be inside the book before looking at the questions. Use the word 'minibeast' and make sure that the children understand its meaning.

9b – Help the children to locate the word 'minibeasts' in the picture and discuss what this means before reading the questions and completing the tasks.

9c – Ask the children how they can predict what a book might be about before they read it. Encourage them to read the text, helping where necessary by cueing in words. Discuss what a blurb is. Look at other examples of blurbs. Help the children to verbalise their answers before they write.

Activity 10 – Y1, Term 2, T11

10a – Read the rhyme, encouraging the children to join in where they can. Go through the tasks and, when completed, help them to recite the rhyme again.

10b – Help the children to read the rhyme with you before they go through the tasks. Help them to look for matching words and to reinforce known and familiar words. Get them to recite the rhyme in pairs.

10c – Read the rhyme all the way through with the children. Help them to break down unfamiliar words and assimilate them. Ask them to think of ways of learning the whole rhyme by heart. Read through the tasks with them before letting them write.

Activity 11 – Y1, Term 2, T9

11a – Go through each picture with the children. Establish that they understand how speech bubbles work; use the word 'dialogue' if appropriate. Help them to verbalise their answers to the tasks.

11b – Ask the children to describe the pictures and predict what the speech bubbles might say. Use the word 'dialogue' where appropriate. Help them to verbalise their answers to the tasks.

11c – Ask the children to read the text, pointing out which parts of it are 'dialogue'. Help them to verbalise their answers before writing.

Activity 12 – Y1, Term 2, T7

12a – The important thing to notice in this picture/story is that if the guinea pig's cage isn't closed, something else will happen. The children need to notice the open cage door and to predict the event.

12b – Make sure the children have noted that Jake hasn't closed the cage door. What do they think might happen in the story?

12c – Help the children to read the text. Point out the ellipsis at the end and go over what this means. Can the children predict what will happen? Get them to verbalise the reason for this event.

Activity 13 – Y1, Term 2, T17

13a – The children need to be able to differentiate fiction from non-fiction. Discuss how they can tell whether something is fiction or non-fiction. Do bears really have parties?

13b – Help the children to read the pictures and verbalise what is happening. Discuss whether the piece is fiction or non-fiction. How can they tell?

13c – The 'story' has 'information' inside it. Help the children to decide whether this makes a text fiction or non-fiction. What do they think is the main element that makes this piece fiction?

Activity 14 – Y1, Term 2, T20

14a – What does this page remind the children of? Help them to locate the matching words and to familiarise themselves with them. Discuss how a list of words could appear in a dictionary.

14b – Discuss the concepts of a dictionary and alphabetical order as appropriate. Help the children to complete the tasks using these two concepts.

14c – Read the text with the children. Help them to understand that it is giving them information. Assist them in verbalising then labelling the picture. Help them to write their words in alphabetical order.

Activity 15 – Y1, Term 3, T1

15a – Discuss 'ing' word endings with the children. Get

them to verbalise all the 'ing's they can see happening. Help them to complete the tasks.

15b – Discuss word endings, especially 'ing'. Read the text with them and help them to work out who is who in the pictures. Let them familiarise themselves with the words so as to complete the rest of the tasks.

15c – Read all the text and questions through with the children. Help them, as appropriate, to reinforce their knowledge and understanding of 'ing' word endings.

Activity 16 – Y1, Term 3, T7

16a – Discuss the concept of blurbs on the back covers of books. Help the children to discern what is happening in the pictures before working on the questions.

16b – Read the text with the children and then look at the pictures. Get them to verbalise all that they can see before working on the tasks with them.

16c – Discuss the idea of blurbs before reading the text with the children. Encourage them to verbalise and discuss together their answers to the questions before writing.

Activity 17 – Y1, Term 3, T19

17a – Talk about facts and information and how they can be shown in books. Is this fiction or non-fiction? Talk about the pictures and encourage the children to tell everything that they can find out from them.

17b – Ask the children if this page is telling a story or giving information and facts. Help them to decide what the information is before they complete the questions.

17c – Read the text with the children and ask them to decide what kind of writing this is. Reinforce the fact that it is non-fiction. How can they tell this? Encourage them to verbalise their answers and to check their facts before completing the tasks.

Activity 18 – Y1, Term 3, T19

18a – Discuss the diagram and show the children which way the cycle goes, following the arrows. Help them to work out what the diagram is telling them. Talk about how useful it is to have labels on the diagram.

18b – Show the children how the diagram goes round clockwise and discuss why this is a good way to show a life cycle. Do they think the labels are helpful? Why? Help them to locate the words they need to complete the tasks.

18c – Look at the diagram with the children and then read the text and discuss it. Help them to locate the information they need to complete the tasks. Do they feel that life cycle diagrams are useful? Why?

Activity 19 – Y1, Term 3, T5

19a – Look at the pictures with the children. Ask them to verbalise exactly what is happening. Encourage them to remember the story and retell it in the right order, checking against the pictures that they are right.

19b – Ask the children to talk about the pictures, noticing everything that is happening. When they have completed the tasks ask them to tell the story in the right order, writing or scribing as appropriate.

19c – Read the text with the children, getting them to discuss it fully before they complete the tasks. Encourage them to retell or rewrite the story, without looking at the text, making sure everything is in the right order.

Activity 20 – Y1, Term 3, T8

20a – Discuss the where and the when of stories and use the word 'setting' where appropriate. Look at the pictures and ask the children to describe what they can see. Help them to choose a setting for their own story which they can tell for you to scribe.

20b – Discuss the idea of settings, reminding the children that these incorporate where and when. Ask them to tell you everything they can see in the pictures before they choose the relevant captions. Help them to choose a setting for their own story which they can tell, write or have scribed.

20c – Read the text with the children and discuss settings. Find out if they understand what the setting of the story in the text is. Encourage them to verbalise all their ideas before completing the tasks.

Activity 21 – Y1, Term 3, T18

21a – Look at the pictures with the children. Read the captions to them and ask them to describe what they can see. Use the words 'first', 'then', 'next', 'in the end', and so on to reinforce them.

21b – Tell the children the pictures are telling a recount of Jake's visit to his gran's. Do they know what a recount is? Help them to understand the use of the words 'first', 'then', 'next', and so on in a recount.

21c – Read the text with the children. What kind of text do they think this is? Help them to understand that although it is a story it is also a recount of Jake's visit to his gran's. In fact, it is a recount written in story form. Help them to locate the answers to the questions in the text.

Activity 22 – Y1, Term 3, T9

22a – Read the poems with the children. There are three different poems about dance. What differences do the children notice about them? The first two questions are for discussion with an adult or in a group. Help them to locate some more poems about dancing.

22b – Read all of the poems with the children, or tape them on a recorder for them to listen to. Ask them to describe what they notice about the poems. Help them to learn and recite their favourite.

22c – All the poems have the same 'theme'. Can the children decide what it is? Help them to find things that are the same and things that are different about the poems. Encourage them to talk about what they like or don't like about them and to choose the one they like best. They could learn it to recite.

Name _____

Three Billy Goats Gruff

Can you see grass?

Yes ☐   No ☐

Can you see three goats?

Yes ☐   No ☐

Can you see a car?

Yes ☐   No ☐

Can you see a bridge?

Yes ☐   No ☐

Can you see a troll?

Yes ☐   No ☐

Can you see an elephant?

Yes ☐   No ☐

✎ What else can you see?

I can see

✎ Draw:

Three goats	A bridge	A troll

Name _____

Three Billy Goats Gruff

✎ Use these words to label the picture:

river

goats

grass

bridge

troll

field

trees

✎ Write the missing words:

The g ___ ___ ___ ___ are in the f ___ ___ ___ ___.

The goats are eating the g ___ ___ ___ ___.

There is a r ___ ___ ___ ___.

The b ___ ___ ___ ___ ___ is over the river.

Under the bridge there is a t ___ ___ ___ ___ .

Should there be an elephant in the picture?

✎ What do you think the troll is doing?

The troll is

Name _____

Three Billy Goats Gruff

Read the story and answer the questions.

Once there were three billy goats. The grass in their field was old. It was not very good to eat. It was not tasty.

The goats wanted to find some new, sweet grass.

The three billy goats set off to find a field where the grass was new and sweet.

Soon they came to a river. And there, on the other side, they saw something wonderful. All they had to do was cross the bridge. But underneath the bridge there lived a troll.

✎ Write in your own words what the old grass was like.

_____

_____

Remember to write in sentences.

✎ Why did the billy goats go on their journey?

_____

✎ What did the billy goats look for? Put a ✔

a) A river ☐   b) Grass that was new and sweet ☐

c) A bigger field ☐   d) A bridge ☐

✎ Which words tell you that the three billy goats went on a journey? _____

✎ The story says three billy goats saw 'something wonderful'. What do you think this could be?

_____

✎ Write or tell the rest of the story.

Name _____

Twinkle, twinkle, little star

Can you see the window?

Yes ☐   No ☐

Can you see the sky?

Yes ☐   No ☐

Can you see the moon?

Yes ☐   No ☐

Can you see the twinkling star?

Yes ☐   No ☐

Can you see Father Christmas on his sleigh?

Yes ☐   No ☐

✎ What else can you see?

I can see

✎ Draw:

Five little stars	One big twinkling star	The moon

• Say the nursery rhyme. Think about the pattern. Can you tap it out?

Name _____

Twinkle, twinkle, little star

✎ Use these words to label the picture:

stars

moon

twinkling

sky

chimney

rooftops

✎ Write the missing words:

Twinkle, twinkle, l __ __ __ __ __ star.

How I wonder what you a __ __!

U __ above the world so high,

Like a diamond in the s __ __.

Do you think there should be a sun in the picture?

✎ What does the rhyme tell you the star is like?

The star is like a

✎ Match the words that rhyme. The first one is done.

bright	star	like	night
moon	sky	are	soon
pie	sprinkle	twinkle	bike

Name _____

Twinkle, twinkle, little star

Twinkle, twinkle, little star,
How I wonder what you are!
Up above the world so high,
Like a diamond in the sky.

When the blazing sun is gone,
When he nothing shines upon,
Then you show your little light,
Twinkle, twinkle, all the night.

✎ Write in your own words why the poet writes
'How I wonder what you are'.

_____

_____

_____

✎ What do you think a 'blazing' sun is?

_____

_____

Remember to write in sentences.

✎ What does the star do? Does it:

a) make the sky dark? ☐   b) show a light? ☐

c) become a diamond? ☐   d) sing a song? ☐

✎ Which words tell you where the star is?

_____

Name _____

Charlotte, the guinea pig

Can you see a cage?	Yes	☐	No ☐
Can you see a guinea pig?	Yes	☐	No ☐
Can you see a water bottle?	Yes	☐	No ☐
Can you see food?	Yes	☐	No ☐
Can you see a label?	Yes	☐	No ☐
Can you see a goldfish?	Yes	☐	No ☐

✎ What else can you see?

I can see

✎ Draw:

A guinea pig	A cage	A label for the cage

Name _____

Charlotte, the guinea pig

✎ Use these words to label the picture, then write a caption for the picture.

cage	straw	water	Charlotte	carrots

✎ Fill in the missing words:

The c __ __ __ is Charlotte's home.

C __ __ __ __ __ __ __ __ is a guinea pig.

She has s __ __ __ __ on the bottom of her cage.

They give her w __ __ __ __ in a bottle.

Charlotte likes to eat c __ __ __ __ __ __.

✎ The teacher is writing a notice. What do you think it will say?

I think the notice will tell the children _____

_____

✎ Should the door of the cage be open or closed? Why?

_____

_____

Remember to write in sentences.

Name _____

Charlotte, the guinea pig

Whose turn is it to look after Charlotte?

Mon   Jas and Sam ✔

Tues   Shahid and Ross ✔

Wed   Emma and Harry

Thurs   William and George

Fri   Josh and Jake

Read the story and answer the questions.

In Mrs Mott's classroom there is a cage. Inside the cage there is a guinea pig. The pet is called Charlotte. The children take turns to look after her. When they have had their turn they tick their names off the list.

✎ Write in your own words what happens to Charlotte in the classroom.

_____

_____

✎ Why is there a notice by the cage?

_____

✎ How do you think the children look after Charlotte? Do they:

a) give her a bath? ☐   b) take her for a walk? ☐

c) make sure she has food and water? ☐   d) read her a story? ☐

✎ What does the list by the cage tell you?

_____

✎ Which day do you think it is in the story? How do you know?

_____

✎ Whose turn will it be to look after Charlotte the next day?

_____

Name _____

Jake's classroom

Can you see Jake's classroom?

Yes ☐   No ☐

Can you see the water play?

Yes ☐   No ☐

Can you see bottles for pouring?

Yes ☐   No ☐

Can you see a colander with holes?

Yes ☐   No ☐

Can you see water dripping?

Yes ☐   No ☐

Can you see a blue whale?

Yes ☐   No ☐

✎ What else can you see?

I can see

✎ Where do you think the water play is happening? Put a ✔

a) In the park ☐   b) In the bath ☐   c) In the classroom ☐

✎ When is it happening?

a) In the morning ☐   b) At teatime ☐   c) At bedtime ☐

✎ Who is playing in the water?

a) The guinea pig ☐   b) The teacher ☐   c) Jake ☐

✎ What sounds is the water making?

a) bang crash! ☐   b) splosh! ☐   c) splash! ☐   d) crrrunch! ☐

Name _____

Jake's classroom

✎ Use these words to label the picture:

classroom

water play

Jake

bottle

things that float

Jake is busy in the water play. There is so much to do!

✎ Fill in the missing words:

Jake is in the

c __ __ __ __ __ __ __ __.

It is his turn for

w __ __ __ __   p __ __ __.

Jake fills the b __ __ __ __ __ with water.

The toys in the water can f __ __ __ __.

The water goes S __ __ __ __ __! S__ __ __ __ __! S__ __ __ __ __!

✎ What time of day do you think it is?

I think it is

✎ Where else could Jake play in the water? Put a ✔

Name _____

Jake's classroom

One morning, in Jake's classroom, it was his turn for water play. Jake loved pouring, splashing and sloshing. He filled up one bottle from another and poured the water out. He liked to watch it drip through the holes in the colander. He enjoyed getting wet.

✎ In your own words, write where the story happened.

_____

_____

✎ Why was Jake doing water play? _____

_____

✎ Why did Jake like the water play? Was it so that he could:

a) get clean? ☐   b) swim? ☐   c) pour and splash and slosh? ☐

d) shout and scream? ☐

✎ Which words tell you what Jake used the colander for?

_____

✎ Which word tells you how Jake felt about getting wet? What does the word mean?

_____

✎ Where else could Jake do water play? Put a ✔

a) At the library? ☐   b) In the supermarket? ☐

c) At the petrol station? ☐   d) In the bath at home? ☐

✎ Start a new story, with Jake playing in the water but not at school. Tell your story to someone and then write it down.

Name _____

Make a mask

What you need:

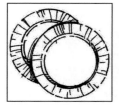  

 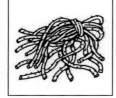 

What you do:

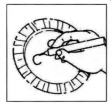 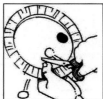   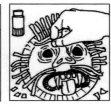 

✎ Look at the things you need to make a mask.

Do you need ?   Yes ☐   No ☐

Do you need ?   Yes ☐   No ☐

Do you need ?   Yes ☐   No ☐

Do you need ?   Yes ☐   No ☐

✎ Should you do this first ?   Yes ☐   No ☐

✎ Should you do this last ?   Yes ☐   No ☐

• Follow the instructions to make a mask of your own.

Name _____

Make a mask

What you need:

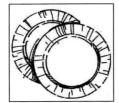   

_____ _____ _____ _____

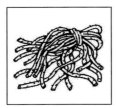 

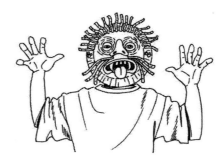

_____ _____

_____

What you do:

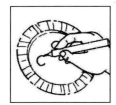   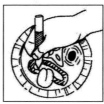  

✎ Use these words to label the first set of pictures:

glue   paper plates   scissors   sticky shapes   pens   wool

✎ Look at these instructions, telling you what to do. Fill in the missing words:

First, you draw two eyes on a p __ __ __ __ p __ __ __ __.

Then you c __ __ them out carefully with s __ __ __ __ __ __ __.

Next, you draw a face with a p __ __.

Then, colour the face.

Next, g __ __ __ bits on.

Last, thread w __ __ __ to tie the mask on.

✎ What do you need the wool for? _____

_____

Name _____

Make a mask

What you need:

- paper plates
- pens
- scissors
- glue
- bits of wool
- sticky shapes

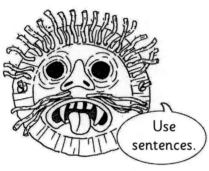

Use sentences.

What you do:

1. Draw two eyes on a plate.
2. Cut out the eyes.
3. Draw a face.
4. Colour it.
5. Stick on bits of wool, paper teeth etc.
6. Thread wool through sides to tie it on with.

✎ Finish this sentence:

These words tell you _____

✎ What do you need to start with?

a) breakfast ☐ b) whiskers ☐ c) pictures of cats ☐ d) paper plates ☐

✎ Where does it tell you how many things you need to collect together?

_____

✎ Is this kind of writing:

a) a story? ☐ b) a poem? ☐ c) information? ☐ d) instructions? ☐

✎ What would happen if everything in the 'What you do' section was in the wrong order?

_____

✎ How could you find out if they are in the right order?

_____

Name _____

The play

The children in Jake's class are doing a play.

Can you see a palm tree?   Yes ☐   No ☐

Can you see four pirates?   Yes ☐   No ☐

Can you see a treasure chest?   Yes ☐   No ☐

Can you see a parrot?   Yes ☐   No ☐

Can you see a spade?   Yes ☐   No ☐

Can you see a police car?   Yes ☐   No ☐

✎ What else can you see?

> I can see

✎ What do you think the mums and dads are doing?

>

- Tell the story.

- Act the play with your friends.

Name _____

The play

The children in Jake's class are doing a play.

✎ Use these words to label the picture:

    map   treasure chest   pirate   parrot

       palm tree   spade   mums and dads

✎ Fill in the missing words:

Jake's class are doing a p ___ ___ ___.

The p ___ ___ ___ ___ ___ ___ are on an island.

They have found the tr ___ ___ ___ ___ ___ ___ ch ___ ___ ___.

Jake has the p ___ ___ ___ ___ ___ .

The m ___ ___ ___ and d ___ ___ ___ all clap.

✎ What do you think the spade is for?

The spade is

✎ Do you think there should be a police car in the picture? Yes ☐ No ☐

✎ Why do you think this? _____

_____

• Tell the story and then act the play.

Name _____

The play

Jake and his friends have made up a play. All the mums and dads have come to see it. The children are pirates on an island. They are looking for treasure. They have a map to tell them where it is buried.

The pirates have a parrot and a spade. The parrot is very noisy. It keeps squawking. The spade is heavy but the pirates need to carry it with them.

✎ Write, in your own words, what the story is about.

_____

_____

_____

✎ Why are there pirates in school? _____

_____

✎ What are the children doing?

a) Making sandcastles ☐   b) Having a holiday ☐

c) Acting a play ☐   d) Looking after a parrot ☐

✎ Which words tell you what the pirates are looking for?

_____

✎ The words say the parrot is being noisy. What is it doing?

_____

✎ Why do you think the pirates need to take the heavy spade with them?

_____

• Make up a play about the pirates and act it out with a group of friends.

Name _____

Bill Bear's birthday party

- Work with a friend.

Can you see Bill Bear?	Yes ☐	No ☐
Can you see lots of post?	Yes ☐	No ☐
Can you see Bill Bear cooking?	Yes ☐	No ☐
Can you see Bill Bear's birthday cards?	Yes ☐	No ☐
Can you see the party?	Yes ☐	No ☐
Can you see a Christmas tree?	Yes ☐	No ☐

✎ What else can you see?

I can see

✎ Join the letters that are the same:

B   A   B   B   D   B   F   B   S

- Say three words that begin with the letter B.

Name _____

Bill Bear's birthday party

✎ Use some of these words to make captions under the pictures:

Getting up   The post   Making jelly   Getting ready   Candle alight

Lots of friends   Birthday cards   Cakes

✎ Do you think it's a good day for Bill Bear?   Yes ☐ No ☐

✎ Why do you think this?

I think

✎ Should there be a Christmas tree in the picture?   Yes ☐ No ☐

✎ Why? _____

✎ Which words go on a birthday card?

Get well soon. ☐   I miss you. ☐ Happy birthday. ☐ Write soon. ☐

• Tell the story.

Name _____

Bill Bear's birthday party

Bill Bear jumped out of bed. It was a very special day. His birthday! He was so excited!

First, Bill Bear opened all his birthday cards. There were so many he couldn't count them all.

He was going to have a party and all his friends were coming. Bill Bear made jelly and cakes. He lit the candle on his birthday cake and waited for his friends to arrive.

Read the story with a friend and answer the questions together.

✎ Write, in your own words, what Bill Bear was going to do.

_____

_____

✎ Why did Bill Bear make jelly and cakes? _____

_____

✎ How did Bill Bear feel?

a) A bit sad ☐   b) Really hungry ☐

c) Ever so tired ☐   d) Really excited ☐

Did you use sentences?

✎ Which words tell you that Bill Bear had a lot of birthday cards?

_____

✎ What does the word 'arrive' mean?

a) Drive ☐   b) Go out ☐

c) Get together ☐   d) Get somewhere ☐

✎ Which word is the odd one out? Why?

birthday party   cards   happy   swim   jelly

Name _____

Jake's great day

This is Jake.

Can you see the field?	Yes ☐	No ☐
Can you see the children?	Yes ☐	No ☐
Are the children in the classroom?	Yes ☐	No ☐
Is there a flag?	Yes ☐	No ☐
Can you see Jake in the big picture?	Yes ☐	No ☐
Is there a dinosaur?	Yes ☐	No ☐

✎ What are the children doing?

The children are

✎ Circle which of these Jake is wearing.

• Tell the story.

Name _____

Jake's great day

el the picture:

school   car park   children

Fill in the missing words:

It is race day at s ___ ___ ___ ___ ___.

The children are on the f ___ ___ ___ ___.

Jake is in a r ___ ___ ___.

The c ___ ___ ___ ___ ___ ___ ___ are shouting.

J ___ ___ ___ is at the front.

Should there be a dinosaur in the picture?

How do you know the children want Jake to win the race?

The children are

Do you think the children like Jake? Why?

_____

_____

_____

Name _____

Jake's great day

Jake loved running. He could run as fast as the wind. One day, at school, there was going to be a race. Every day Jake worked hard at his running. He really wanted to win.

On the day of the race, all the children stood at the side of the field.

The runners lined up.

Off they went. Jake ran and ran and ran. All the children were chanting, 'Jake! Jake! Jake!'

✎ What did Jake love to do?

a) Play football ☐   b) Skip ☐   c) Run ☐   d) Dance ☐

✎ What was happening at school?

a) A play ☐   b) A race ☐

c) Swimming ☐   d) A book fair ☐

Remember to write in sentences.

✎ How fast could Jake run?

_____

✎ Which sentence tells you that Jake did lots of running practice?

_____

✎ What word in the story means 'shouting'? _____

✎ Why do you think the children were shouting Jake's name?

_____

✎ Write or tell the rest of the story.

Name _____

The new books

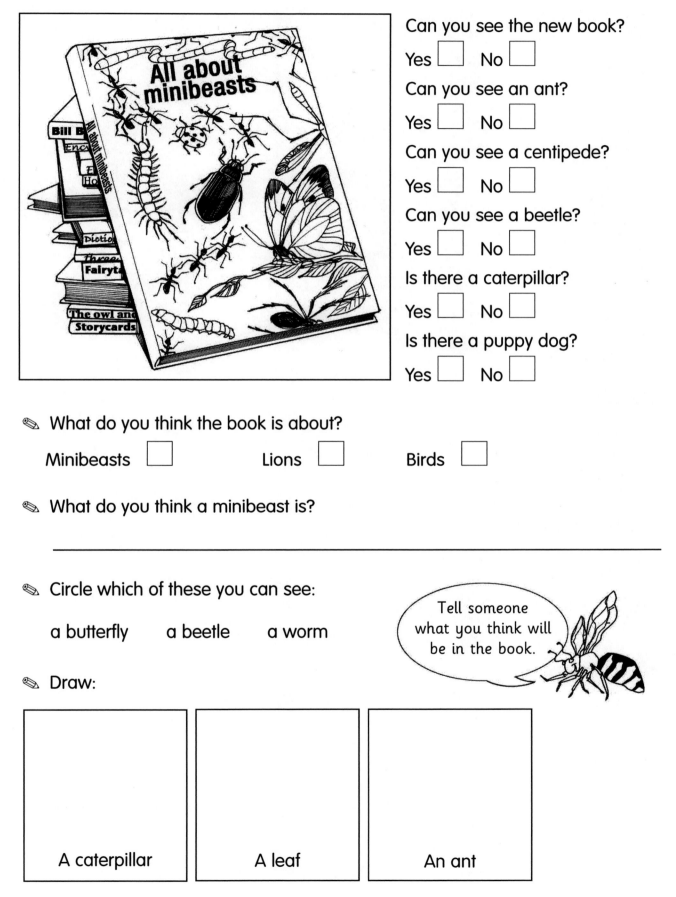

Can you see the new book?

Yes ☐   No ☐

Can you see an ant?

Yes ☐   No ☐

Can you see a centipede?

Yes ☐   No ☐

Can you see a beetle?

Yes ☐   No ☐

Is there a caterpillar?

Yes ☐   No ☐

Is there a puppy dog?

Yes ☐   No ☐

✎ What do you think the book is about?

Minibeasts ☐   Lions ☐   Birds ☐

✎ What do you think a minibeast is?

_____

✎ Circle which of these you can see:

a butterfly   a beetle   a worm

Tell someone what you think will be in the book.

✎ Draw:

A caterpillar	A leaf	An ant

Name _____

The new books

✎ Use these words to label the pictures on the book:

caterpillar

ant

beetle

centipede

butterfly

worm

Should there be a crocodile in the picture?

✎ Fill in the missing words:

The children have some new b ___ ___ ___ ___ .

There are p ___ ___ ___ ___ ___ ___ ___ on the covers.

There is a picture of an a ___ ___ .

There is a picture of a c e ___ ___ ___ ___ ___ ___ ___ .

There is a picture of a b e ___ ___ ___ ___ .

✎ What do you think the minibeast book will tell you?

Where minibeasts live?   Yes ☐   No ☐

What minibeasts eat?   Yes ☐   No ☐

What kinds of minibeasts there are?   Yes ☐   No ☐

How many legs minibeasts have?   Yes ☐   No ☐

✎ Think of some creatures that might be in the book. Draw some minibeasts of your own and label them.

Name _____

The new books

This book has a picture of minibeasts on the cover, as well as its title and the author's name.

The blurb says:

Learn all about 'Habitats'. This book tells you 'Where to look'. It also tells you all about 'The hunt for food'.

The book has a clear contents page and a good index.

It introduces minibeasts you may not have met before.

Find out everything you need to know about the different creatures that live all around us.

✎ What kind of book is the text telling you about?

a) A story book ☐   b) A poetry book ☐

c) An information book ☐   d) A diary ☐

✎ How do you know this? _____

_____

✎ Which word in the text is a word that means 'animals'?

_____

✎ Which part of the book might tell you what different kinds of minibeasts eat?

_____

✎ What will the part of the book with the heading 'Where to look' tell you?

_____

✎ What does the text mean when it says the book has 'a good index'?

_____

✎ On the back of this sheet, list of all the minibeasts that might be in the book.

Name _____

The Owl and the Pussy Cat

The owl and the pussy cat went to sea

In a beautiful pea green boat.

They took some honey

And plenty of money

Wrapped up in a five pound note.

✎ Can you see:

The owl? Yes ☐ No ☐

The pussy cat? Yes ☐ No ☐

The boat? Yes ☐ No ☐

A jar of honey? Yes ☐ No ☐

The moon? Yes ☐ No ☐

An aeroplane? Yes ☐ No ☐

✎ What are the owl and the pussy cat doing?

The owl and the pussy cat are

✎ Circle which of these the owl and the pussy cat have in the boat:

some toast   some honey

some tomato sauce   a piano

Learn the rhyme.
Say it with a friend.

✎ Draw:

| The owl | The boat | The pussy cat |

Name _____

The Owl and the Pussy Cat

✎ Use these words to label the picture:

owl   pussy cat   boat
honey   money

> The owl and the pussy cat went
> to sea
> In a beautiful pea green boat.
> They took some honey
> And plenty of money
> Wrapped up in a five pound note.

✎ Fill in the missing words:

The o ___ ___ and the pussy c ___ ___ went to sea
In a beautiful pea green b ___ ___ ___.
They took some h ___ ___ ___ ___
And plenty of m ___ ___ ___ ___
Wrapped up in a f ___ ___ ___ pound note.

✎ What do you think the words 'went to sea' mean?

I think the words mean _____

_____

✎ Why is there a moon in the picture?

There is a moon because _____

_____

• Learn the rhyme by heart. Recite it with a friend.
• Ask someone to tell you the rest of the rhyme. Learn that, too.

Name _____

The Owl and the Pussy Cat

The owl and the pussy cat went to sea
In a beautiful pea green boat.
They took some honey and plenty of money,
Wrapped up in a five pound note.

The owl looked up to the stars above
And sang to a small guitar,
'Oh lovely pussy, oh pussy my love,
What a beautiful pussy you are, you are,
What a beautiful pussy you are.

They sailed away for a year and a day
To the land where the bong tree grows.
And there, in a wood, a piggy-wig stood,
With a ring at the end of his nose, his nose,
With a ring at the end of his nose.

There is more to this rhyme. Find out how it ends.

✎ Write in your own words what the rhyme is about. _____

_____

_____

✎ Write in your own words what 'went to sea' means. _____

_____

✎ Why do you think the owl and the pussy cat sailed away together?

　　a) To go fishing ☐　　b) Because they liked looking for pigs ☐

　　c) To spend money ☐　　d) Because they liked being together ☐

✎ Which words tell you that the journey took a long time?

_____

✎ Which words rhyme with:
　　a) boat _____　　b) above _____　　c) wood _____　　d) grows _____

Name _____

The Three Bears

Can you see Baby Bear?   Yes ☐   No ☐

How many times?   1 ☐   2 ☐   3 ☐

Can you see Mummy Bear?   Yes ☐   No ☐

How many times?   1 ☐   2 ☐   3 ☐

Can you see Daddy Bear?   Yes ☐   No ☐

How many times?   1 ☐   2 ☐   3 ☐

Can you see Goldilocks?   Yes ☐   No ☐

How many times?   1 ☐   2 ☐   3 ☐

What do you think Goldilocks will say when she wakes up? Draw a speech bubble for the words.

✎ In the first picture, who is talking?

_____

✎ In the second picture, what does Daddy Bear say?

_____

✎ In the third picture, what does Baby Bear say?

_____

✎ What do you think happens next?

_____

Name _____

The Three Bears

✎ Fill in the missing words:

Baby Bear has a small ch ___ ___ ___.

Daddy Bear has the biggest ch ___ ___ ___ .

Mummy Bear has a medium-sized b ___ ___ .

What do you think Goldilocks will say when she wakes up?

✎ Read the speech bubbles in the picture story.

Who says, 'Who's been sitting in my chair?' _____

What does Mummy Bear say?

_____

What does Baby Bear say?

_____

✎ Do you think Goldilocks is cosy in Baby Bear's bed? _____

How do you know? _____

✎ Where is the picture story happening?

a) Outside the cottage ☐   b) Inside the cottage ☐

✎ Tell or write the story. Tell all the things you think the Bears say.

Name _____

The Three Bears

Once upon a time there were three bears. They lived in a cottage in the woods. One day they went for a walk. When they came home, to their surprise, they saw that someone had been in the house.
They looked at their bowls.
'Who's been eating my porridge?' growled Daddy Bear.
'Who's been eating my porridge?' asked Mummy Bear.
'Who's been eating my porridge?' squeaked Baby Bear.
'And they've eaten it all up!'
They looked at their chairs.
'Who's been sitting in my chair?' growled Daddy Bear.
'Who's been sitting in my chair?' asked Mummy Bear.
'Who's been sitting in my chair?' squeaked Baby Bear.
'And they've broken it all up!'

✎ Write, in your own words, who lives in the cottage in the woods.

_____

✎ Where had the bears been?

The bears had been _____

✎ Why were they surprised when they came home?

The bears were surprised because _____

_____

✎ What did the Bears say?

a) Who's been in our house? ☐ b) Who's been eating the cornflakes? ☐

c) Who's been sitting in my chair? ☐ d) Who's been lying on my cushion? ☐

✎ There are three words in the story which mean 'said'. Which words are they?

_____   _____   _____

✎ Use these words to write, on the back of this sheet, what happens when the Bears go into the bedroom.

✎ Make a comic strip of the story, using speech bubbles.

Name _____

Home time!

Can you see the guinea pig?   Yes ☐   No ☐

Can you see Jake near the cage?   Yes ☐   No ☐

Can you see Jake's mum?   Yes ☐   No ☐

Has Jake fastened the cage door?   Yes ☐   No ☐

✎ Are the children getting ready to go home? _____

✎ How do you know? _____

_____

✎ What do you think will happen? _____

_____

✎ Why do you think this? _____

✎ On the back of this sheet, draw the guinea pig coming out of her cage.

• Tell the story of the picture and what you think happens next.

Name _____

Home time!

Have a good look at the picture. Tell everything you can see.

✎ Write a caption underneath the picture. Choose from:

It's almost time to go home.

The children are tidying the room.

Jake gives Charlotte some clean water.

Don't forget to close the cage door, Jake!

✎ Write a caption of your own.

✎ What do you think might happen next in the story?

_____

✎ Why do you think this?

_____

✎ On the back of this sheet, make up some sentences that tell the whole story.

Name _____

Home time!

It was almost time to go home. Mrs Mott and the children made the classroom tidy. Jake was putting water into Charlotte's bottle so that she would have something to drink when everyone had gone.

Just then Jake's mum came to the door. 'Jake!' called Mrs Mott. 'Your mum's here. You need to go early today.'

Jake rushed to get his coat and his bag. Off they went.

'Now then, children,' said Mrs Mott. 'Let's all sit down and have a quiet time before the bell goes.'

Nobody noticed that something was wrong.

✎ Write, in your own words, what part of the day it was in the story.

_____

✎ What were the children doing?

_____

✎ Why did Jake put water in Charlotte's bottle? Was it because:

a) she was hungry? ☐   b) she was a guinea pig? ☐

c) the bottle was clean? ☐   d) she would need a drink later? ☐

✎ Which word tells you that Jake was in a hurry? _____

✎ What do you think was the thing that nobody noticed?

_____

✎ What do you think might happen?

_____

✎ What might happen next?

_____

✎ Make up your own ending to the story. Write it down or tell it to someone.

Name _____

Bill Bear plans his birthday party

Can you see a birthday party invitation?   Yes ☐ No ☐

Can you see Bill Bear writing it?   Yes ☐ No ☐

Can you see Bill Bear posting the invitation?   Yes ☐ No ☐

Can you see Bill Bear with his birthday cake?   Yes ☐ No ☐

Can you see the children coming to the party?   Yes ☐ No ☐

Can you see the map on the invitation?   Yes ☐ No ☐

✎ What will it tell the children? _____

_____

✎ Is this a kind of story? _____

✎ How do you know? _____

Is it fiction?   Yes ☐ No ☐   Is it non-fiction?   Yes ☐ No ☐

✎ Make an invitation to Bill Bear's birthday party. Write your own name on it.

Name _____

Bill Bear plans his birthday party

Have a good look at the pictures. Tell everything you can see.

✎ Write captions for the pictures.

✎ Finish these sentences:

There is an invitation to _____

Bill Bear writes _____

Bill Bear posts _____

The map will tell everyone _____

✎ Is this a story? Yes ☐ No ☐ Or is it information? Yes ☐ No ☐

✎ What is a story called? Fiction ☐ Non-fiction ☐

✎ What is information called? Fiction ☐ Non-fiction ☐

Name _____

Bill Bear plans his birthday party

One day Bill Bear was writing jolly invitations for his birthday party. This is the information that he put on his invitations:

The time of the party.

The day of the party.

What kind of party it was.

Where the party was.

Just as he finished, he remembered one more thing that needed to go on. A map! He needed to draw a map so that everyone would know where his house was.

Finished at last, Bill Bear went off to post his invitations.

✎ Write, in your own words, what Bill Bear is up to.

_____

✎ Why is Bill Bear making his invitations jolly? Is it so that:

a) his friends will like them ☐   b) they look nice ☐

c) it will keep him busy ☐   d) everyone will come to the party ☐

✎ Why does Bill Bear put information on his invitation?

_____

✎ Why do you think he draws a map?

_____

✎ What kind of writing is this text? Is it:

a) information ☐   b) an invitation ☐

c) a story ☐   d) dialogue ☐

✎ Do you think this writing is: fiction ☐   or   non-fiction ☐

✎ What makes you think this?

_____

Name _____

Simple dictionaries

a b c d e f g h i j k l m n o p q r s t u v w x y z

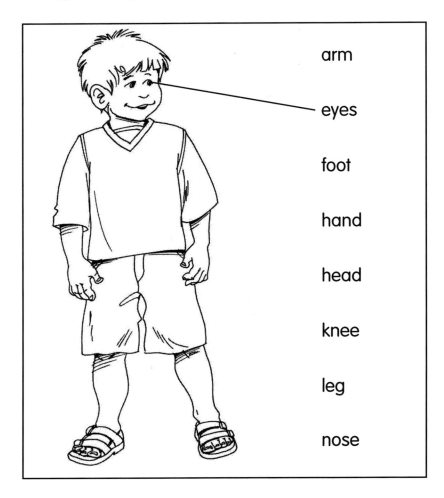

arm

eyes

foot

hand

head

knee

leg

nose

This is a page from a dictionary. It tells you body words.

✎ Match the words to the body. One has been done for you.

✎ Can you see:

The boy's head? Yes ☐ No ☐

The boy's eyes? Yes ☐ No ☐

The boy's foot? Yes ☐ No ☐

The boy's hand? Yes ☐ No ☐

The boy's elbow? Yes ☐ No ☐

What else can you see?

....

Name _____

Simple dictionaries

a b c d e f g h i j k l m n o p q r s t u v w x y z

This page from a dictionary is giving you body words.

✎ Use these words to label the picture:

arm, eyes, foot, hand, head, knee

✎ There are two lines still empty. Label the two body parts.

✎ Make a list of the words and put these two new words into the list.
Make sure you get them in the right order. Where should they go?

✎ Make a dictionary page of your own, for a set of clothes.

Name _____

Simple dictionaries

a b c d e f g h i j k l m n o p q r s t u v w x y z

A dictionary gives you lists of words. Sometimes it gives you their meanings.

This is a page from a dictionary. It is giving you body words. Instead of telling you what each word means, it gives you a diagram.

In a dictionary, the words are written in a special order. The alphabet is written across the top of this page to help you get words in the right order. It is called 'alphabetical order'. This means that you look at the first letter of each word and then write them down in the order that the first letters would appear in the alphabet.

Alphabetical order is very helpful when you are looking up words and meanings.

✎ Fill in the parts of the body with the correct words. Then make a list of the words in the order that you would find them on a dictionary page.

_____

_____

✎ What do you think might happen in a dictionary when two words begin with the same letter?

_____

✎ Do you think alphabetical order is useful? _____

✎ Make a dictionary page of your own, using diagrams, labels and lists. You could choose from: clothes, food, toys.

Name _____

Which words?

Can you see Emma reading a book?   Yes ☐   No ☐

Can you see Jake painting a picture?   Yes ☐   No ☐

Can you see Ahmad writing a story?   Yes ☐   No ☐

Can you see Sophie counting blocks?   Yes ☐   No ☐

Can you see Charlotte in her cage?   Yes ☐   No ☐

✎ Which picture is Ahmad?   Write his name in the box.

✎ Which picture is Sophie?   Write her name in the box.

✎ Which picture is Jake?   Write his name in the box.

✎ Which picture is Emma?   Write her name in the box.

✎ Where is Charlotte?

Charlotte is in her ___ ___ ___ ___.

✎ Draw lines to match the children with what they are doing:

Ahmad   Sophie   Emma   Jake

reading   painting   counting   writing

Name _____

Which words?

What can you see?

Emma is reading a book. Jake is painting a picture. Ahmad is writing a story.

Sophie is counting blocks. Charlotte is in her cage.

✎ Write the children's names under their pictures.

✎ Fill in the missing words:

Emma is r ___ ___ ___ ___ ___ ___.

Jake is p ___ ___ ___ ___ ___ ___ ___.

Ahmad is wr ___ ___ ___ ___ ___ .

Sophie is c ___ ___ ___ ___ ___ ___ g.

Charlotte is in her c ___ ___ ___ .

✎ Match these words and the children to what they are doing:

book	blocks	story	picture
writing	painting	reading	counting
Sophie	Ahmad	Emma	Jake

Name _____

Which words?

Everyone is busy in the classroom. The children can choose what they want to do.

Jake thinks painting a picture would be fun. Emma thinks reading a book would be better. Ahmad thinks writing a story is what he wants to do. Sophie likes counting the number blocks best.

While the children are busy, Charlotte, the guinea pig, is having a snooze in her cage.

Everyone is getting on with their work and being quiet. What a good day it is in the classroom!

✎ Write, in your own words, what's happening in the story.

_____

_____

_____

✎ Why are the children doing different things? Is it because:

a) they are in the classroom? ☐   b) they are all busy? ☐

c) they can choose what to do? ☐   d) they are all friends? ☐

✎ Which words tell you that Charlotte is asleep? _____

✎ Make these words into 'ing' words:

read _____

paint _____

write _____

count _____

sleep _____

choose _____

snooze _____

• Think of four more 'ing' words that you might do at school.

Name _____

Jake's best story

Can you see Jake?   Yes ☐   No ☐

Can you see Jake's book?   Yes ☐   No ☐

Can you see Sam the Spider? Yes ☐   No ☐

Can you see the kitchen?   Yes ☐   No ☐

Can you see the bedroom?   Yes ☐   No ☐

Can you see the garden?   Yes ☐   No ☐

Draw a spider.

✎ What else can you see?

I can see

✎ Look at the pictures. What do you think the story is about?

_____

_____

• Why do you think Jake looks so pleased with himself?

Name _____

Jake's best story

This is a book Jake has written. He is very pleased with himself. The title and the author are written on the front cover. On the back cover Jake has drawn a blurb.

✎ Use these words to write captions: The front cover   The back cover

✎ Fill in the missing words:

Jake has written a b ___ ___ ___.

The t ___ ___ ___ ___ is on the front cover.

The author's n ___ ___ ___ is on the front cover.

On the back cover is the b ___ ___ ___ ___.

✎ Which words tell you that Jake is happy?

_____

✎ Look at the blurb. What do you think the story is about?

_____

✎ What do you think happens next? Why?

_____

_____

Name _____

Jake's best story

Jake has made a new book. In it is his very best story.

On the front cover Jake writes, 'Sam's Escape by Jake'.

On the back cover he writes his blurb. This is what the blurb says:

When Sam the hairy spider escapes from Ben's pocket, Ben's mum is very scared. They search in the kitchen for Sam. They search in the bedroom for Sam. They search in the bathroom for Sam.

You will never guess where they find him!

✎ Write in your own words what this writing is telling you about.

_____

_____

_____

✎ What is the title of the book? _____

_____

✎ Where is the blurb? _____

_____

✎ Who has written the book? Is it:

a) Sam? ☐   b) Ben? ☐

c) Mum? ☐   d) Jake? ☐

Did you write in sentences?

✎ Who is Ben? Is he:

a) the spider? ☐   b) the writer of the story? ☐

b) the boy in the story? ☐   d) Jake's friend? ☐

✎ Why do you think his mum is scared? _____

_____

✎ Where do you think they might find Sam? _____

_____

Name _____

Guinea pig facts

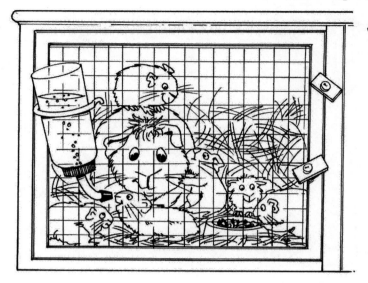

✎ Draw lines to match the words to the things in the picture:

guinea pig
food
cage
straw
babies

Tell someone what facts you can find in the picture.

Look at these pictures. What can you see?

I can see _____

_____

I can see _____

_____

I can see _____

_____

✎ Two of these pictures do not show facts about real guinea pigs. Which ones?

1. ☐   2. ☐   3. ☐

✎ Why are they wrong? <u>They are wrong because guinea pigs</u>

_____

_____

Name _____

Guinea pig facts

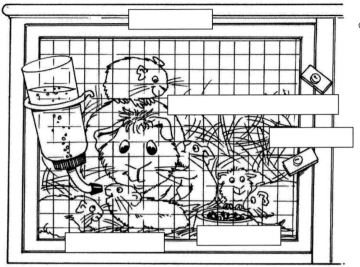

✎ Use these words to label the picture:

guinea pig
food
cage
straw
babies

✎ This is a fact sheet about guinea pigs. Fill in the missing words:

Guinea p ___ ___ ___ are good to have as pets.

Guinea pigs should be kept in a c ___ ___ ___.

Guinea pigs need s ___ ___ ___ ___ for their bedding.

Guinea pigs eat guinea pig f ___ ___ ___.

Guinea pigs have b ___ ___ ___ ___ ___ who are just like them.

✎ You can find out five facts about guinea pigs from this page. What are they? Write them in your own words.

_____

_____

_____

_____

✎ Make a little book of guinea pig facts.

··················

Name _____

Guinea pig facts

Here is some information about guinea pigs.

Guinea pig fact file

- Guinea pigs are rodents.
- They are good tempered, so they make good pets.
- They are herbivores; they eat grains and vegetables.
- They are mammals; they give birth to live babies.
- They can be 21cm to 38cm long.
- They live between three and six years.

✎ Write, in a proper sentence, what this information is about.

_____

✎ What kind of animals are guinea pigs? Are they:

a) reptiles? ☐   b) insects? ☐

c) fish? ☐   d) mammals? ☐

Remember to write in sentences.

✎ Why are guinea pigs good to have as pets?

_____

✎ How long is a small adult guinea pig?

_____

✎ Do guinea pigs lay eggs? Yes ☐ No ☐

✎ How do you know? _____

_____

✎ Which word tells you what kind of eaters guinea pigs are? _____

✎ How old would a really old guinea pig be? _____

_____

✎ Write a fact file like this about birds.

Name ————————————————

The life cycle of a frog

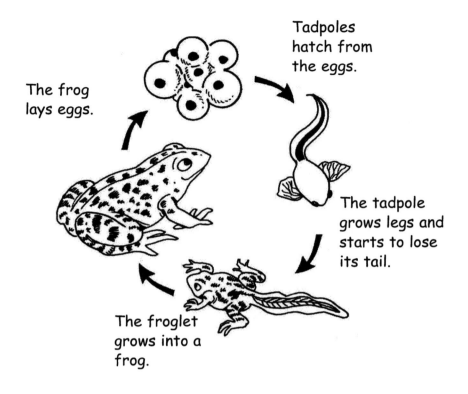

The frog lays eggs.

Tadpoles hatch from the eggs.

The tadpole grows legs and starts to lose its tail.

The froglet grows into a frog.

Can you see the frog?   Yes ☐   No ☐

Can you see the eggs the frog has laid?   Yes ☐   No ☐

Can you see the tadpole?   Yes ☐   No ☐

Can you see the tadpole with legs?   Yes ☐   No ☐

✎ Draw a little frog in this box.

| |
| |

✎ On another sheet draw:

Some frogspawn

A tadpole without legs

A tadpole with legs

✎ Ask someone to help you label your pictures.

Name _____

The life cycle of a frog

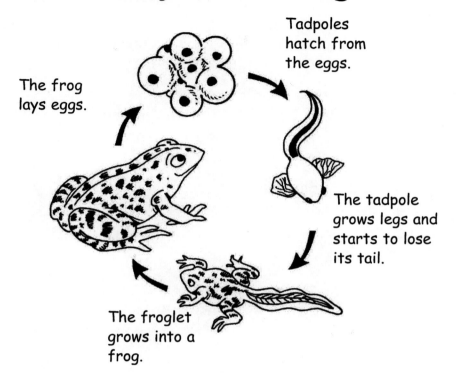

Tadpoles hatch from the eggs.

The frog lays eggs.

The tadpole grows legs and starts to lose its tail.

The froglet grows into a frog.

Look carefully at the diagram and follow the arrows.

Read the words that are by each piece of the diagram.

✎ Which part of the life cycle is the start of the life of a frog?

_____

✎ Fill in the missing words:

The adult frog l ___ ___ ___ eggs.

The e ___ ___ ___ are called frogspawn.

The t ___ ___ ___ ___ ___ ___ ___ hatch out of the eggs.

The tadpoles grow l ___ ___ ___.

The tadpoles change into fr ___ ___ ___ ___ ___ ___.

✎ Draw the life cycle yourself and explain it to someone. Label your diagram.

✎ Draw the life cycle of a butterfly in the same way.

Name _____

The life cycle of a frog

A life cycle tells you about a creature's life, from birth to death. This diagram is showing you the life cycle of a frog.

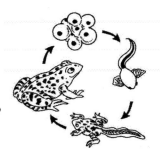

You need two adult frogs to start new frogs. They mate and the female frog lays lots of eggs. This is called frogspawn. The frogspawn sinks to the bottom of the pond, then floats back up again.

The eggs hatch into tadpoles. There are dozens of them. Many of them are eaten by fish or other creatures.

The tadpoles that stay alive begin to grow back legs, then front legs. Their tails get smaller and smaller.

The tadpoles turn into froglets. They spend their days catching flies and growing. When they are adults the cycle begins all over again.

✎ What is this writing telling you about?

_____

✎ What is a life cycle?

_____

✎ What is the writing giving you?

a) Rhyme ☐   b) Illustration ☐

c) Punctuation ☐   d) Information ☐

✎ Why do you think the word 'cycle' is in 'life cycle'?

_____

✎ Which words tell you that many of the tadpoles do not stay alive?

_____

✎ How many legs do the tadpoles grow?

_____

✎ Draw a diagram like the one at the top of the page then label it.

✎ On the back of this sheet, do the life cycle of a butterfly in the same way.

Did you use sentences?

Name _____

Jake goes shopping

Can you see Mum and Jake?   Yes ☐ No ☐

Can you see the bus to town?   Yes ☐ No ☐

Can you see Jake's new tee shirt?   Yes ☐ No ☐

Can you see Jake trying on trainers?   Yes ☐ No ☐

Do you think Jake is choosing a new pair?   Yes ☐ No ☐

Does he like them?   Yes ☐ No ☐

✎ How can you tell? _____

_____

✎ Finish this sentence:

All the way home, Jake kept looking at the new trainers because

_____

• Tell the story. Make sure you say it in the right order.

Name _____

Jake goes shopping

✎ Use these captions to fill in the boxes. Make sure the words fit the pictures.

The new trainers.

Going shopping.

Jake is proud.

Mum buys a tee shirt.

Going on the bus.

✎ Do you think Jake likes the new trainers? How can you tell from the pictures? How can you tell from the words?

_____

_____

✎ Write or tell the story in your own words. Make sure you get it all in the right order.

Name _____

Jake goes shopping

It's Saturday. Mum and Jake are going on a shopping trip. They catch the bus into town.

First, they buy a new tee shirt. Then they go to the shoe shop to buy Jake some new trainers. He tries on seven different pairs of trainers. Mum says, 'This is one pair for every day of the week!'

At last he chooses the ones he likes best. They are brilliant!

Jake keeps the trainers on to go home. He keeps looking at them, all the way, because he likes them so much!

✎ What kind of trip does the story tell you about? Put a ✔

　a) A school trip. ☐　　b) A shopping trip. ☐

　c) A seaside trip. ☐　　d) A coach trip. ☐

Don't forget to write in sentences.

✎ How do Mum and Jake get to town?

_____

✎ What do they buy first?

_____

✎ Which words tell you that Jake can't decide which trainers to have?

_____

✎ Which ones does he choose in the end?

_____

✎ Why does Jake keep looking at the trainers on the way home?

_____

✎ Make a list of what happened in the story in the correct order.

Name _____

Which shall we choose?

Can you see Bill Bear in the park, when it is sunny?   Yes ☐   No ☐

Can you see Bill Bear in the park, when it is raining?   Yes ☐   No ☐

Can you see Bill Bear at home, having a party?   Yes ☐   No ☐

Can you see Bill Bear in the garden with his friends?   Yes ☐   No ☐

Can you see Bill Bear skating?   Yes ☐   No ☐

Can you see Bill Bear swimming?   Yes ☐   No ☐

✎ If you were going to write a Bill Bear story, which one would you choose?

_____

✎ Why? _____

_____

_____

- Tell your story. Begin: One day, Bill Bear…

Name _____

Which shall we choose?

✎ Which caption should you write in which box? Write them in.

Bill Bear at the skating rink.

Bill Bear in the garden.

Bill Bear's birthday party.

Bill Bear in the park on a sunny day.

Bill Bear at his friend's house.

Bill Bear at the swimming pool.

Bill Bear in the park on a rainy day.

✎ If you were going to write a Bill Bear story, which one of these would you choose to write about? Say why.

_____

_____

✎ Choose the one you like best and tell, or write, your story.

Name _____

Which shall we choose?

Mrs Mott's class are making a book. They are going to write a story about Bill Bear having an exciting day. They are thinking about the setting. They are trying to decide where the story will happen.

The children have lots of ideas. 'It could be about a day at the park,' says Sophie. 'It could be a nice, sunny day and everyone could be there.'

'It could be a rainy day at the park,' says Ajay. 'And everyone's stayed at home.'

Emma says, 'I think it should be about Bill Bear's birthday party, at his house.'

'Or it could be about his friends coming round to play in the garden,' says Jake.

'It could be about,' says Mrs Mott, 'Bill Bear going to the ice rink. Or the swimming baths. Or to his friend's house.'

So many ideas! Which one will the children choose?

✎ Who will be the main character in the book?

_____

✎ What will the book be about?

_____

✎ Is the book going to be:

Fiction? ☐   Non-fiction? ☐

✎ How do you know? ————————————————————————

_____

✎ Explain what a setting is.

_____

✎ On the back of this sheet, list all the different settings the class have thought of.

✎ If one idea is the same place as another idea but the weather is different, should you count it as one setting or two? Why?

_____

_____

✎ Choose your favourite setting and write the story.

Name _____

Jake's visit

Mum and Jake are walking in the woods.

Gran and her dog meet them.

Jake throws a ball. The dog chases it.

The dog is tired.

They have little cakes made by Gran.

Gran walks back a little way with them.

This story is about Jake and Mum going to Gran's.

Tell the story.

✎ Draw:

The little dog	The woods	The little cakes

Name _____

Jake's visit

✎ Put these captions in the right boxes:

The dog was tired.

They all met in the woods.

Jake threw the ball.

They had cakes for tea.

Mum and Jake walked in the woods.

They took the ball to throw.

- Tell this story again, keeping it in the right order.

✎ You could make a little book about it.

Name _____

Jake's visit

One Sunday afternoon, Jake and his mum were going to visit Gran. First, they had to walk through the woods. Gran and her little dog, Toby, met them in the middle.

Toby was very pleased to see Jake. Jake gave him a good fuss, then he threw the ball for him. When he threw it, Toby chased after it to fetch it back. He dropped the ball at Jake's feet. Then Jake threw it for him again.

It was a good game for a little dog. By the time he reached Gran's all he could do was flop down for a good sleep. The rest of them had little cakes for tea.

Then it was time for home. Gran and Toby went a little way with them. They took the ball for a replay.

✎ What day was the visit?

_____

✎ How did Mum and Jake get to Gran's?

_____

✎ Which words tell you that Jake and his mum were halfway through the woods when they met Gran and Toby?

_____

✎ Who was the ball game good for?

a) gran? ☐   b) Jake? ☐

c) mum? ☐   d) Toby? ☐

Remember to write in sentences.

✎ Was Toby tired after the game?   Yes ☐ No ☐

✎ How do you know?

_____

✎ What does 'a replay' mean?

_____

✎ Write a recount of a day you went on a visit.

Name _____

Come, dance with me

Dance with me

On my tiptoes
Stretch up high
Reach my fingers
To the sky.
Hear the music
Feel the flow
Hop and skip,
Come on – let's go!
Dance with me.

I am the dance

I am the dance
Spinning round and round,
Swirling, twirling,
Fluttering and floating
To the ground.

Longing to dance

One little mole
Came up above ground,
Blinked in the bright light,
Looked all around.
Liked what he saw
And took the chance
To cartwheel in the sunshine
And join in the dance.

What are all of these poems about?

Which poem is your favourite? Why?

✎ Which words rhyme? Put a ✔

high, sky ☐   flow, go ☐   skip, me ☐

swirling, twirling ☐   dance, round ☐

✎ Find a word that rhymes with:

light _____   chance _____

• Listen to the words and dance the dances.

Name _____

Come, dance with me

Dance with me

On my tiptoes
Stretch up high
Reach my fingers
To the sky.
Hear the music
Feel the flow
Hop and skip,
Come on – let's go!
Dance with me.

I am the dance

I am the dance
Spinning round and round,
Swirling, twirling,
Fluttering and floating
To the ground.

Longing to dance

One little mole
Came up above ground,
Blinked in the bright light,
Looked all around.
Liked what he saw
And took the chance
To cartwheel in the sunshine
And join in the dance.

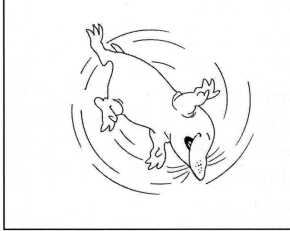

✎ What are all of these poems about?

_____

✎ How do they make you feel?

_____

✎ What did the mole do when he came out of the dark?

_____

✎ Find six pairs of words that rhyme.

_____

• Read the words and dance the actions.

Name _____

Come, dance with me

Dance with me

On my tiptoes
Stretch up high
Reach my fingers
To the sky.
Hear the music
Feel the flow
Hop and skip,
Come on – let's go!
Dance with me.

I am the dance

I am the dance
Spinning round and round,
Swirling, twirling,
Fluttering and floating
To the ground.

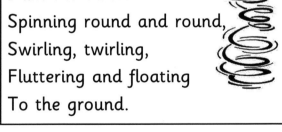

Dance

Hop and skip
And leap up high –
Stretch your fingers
To the sky.

Longing to dance

One little mole
Came up above ground,
Blinked in the bright
    light,
Looked all around.
Liked what he saw
And took the chance
To cartwheel in the sunshine
And join in the dance.

✎ What are all of these poems about?

a) the dark ☐   b) singing ☐   c) moles ☐   d) dancing ☐

✎ Which poem do you think is the best one? Why?

_____

_____

✎ Find and write all the 'dancing' words.

_____

_____

✎ Write the different sets of rhyming words on the back of this sheet.

✎ Write a dance poem of your own, using some of the words.